Spunky Revolutionary War Heroine

Spunky Revolutionary War Heroine

Idella Bodie

SANDLAPPER PUBLISHING CO., INC.

Second Printing, 2003

Published by Sandlapper Publishing Co., Inc.
        Orangeburg, South Carolina

Manufactured in the United States of America

Library of Congress Cataloging-in-Publication Data

Bodie, Idella
        Spunky Revolutionary War heroine / Idella Bodie.
            p. cm. — (Heroes and heroines of the American Revolution)
        Includes bibliographical references (p.).
        ISBN 0-87844-154-9
            1. Langston, Laodicea, 1765 or 6-1837—Juvenile literature. 2. Women
spies—United States—Biography—Juvenile literature. 3. Spies—United
States—Biography—Juvenile literature. 4. United States—History—Revolution,
1775-1783—Secret service—Juvenile literature. 5. United States—History—
Revolution, 1775-1783—Biography—Juvenile literature. 6. United States—
History—Revolution, 1775-1783—Participation, Female—Juvenile literature.
[1. Langston, Laodicea, 1765 or 6-1837. 2. Spies. 3. United States—History—
Revolution, 1775-1783. 4. Women—Biography.] I. Title.

E280.L36 B63 2000
973.3'85—dc21

                                                                    00-036578

To The Young Reader

During the Revolutionary War powerful England, with its shiny new guns and uniforms, fought the colonists who had little money, rifles, or ammunition.

Actually, very few of the soldiers who fought in this war were from England. The colonists who wanted freedom from their mother country fought against other colonists who wanted to remain loyal to the king of England.

Because this was true, Patriot neighbors fought against Tory neighbors. In the Up Country of South Carolina, Tory families outnumbered the Patriots. The family of Solomon Langston was one of the Patriot families who lived among the Tories.

Solomon's only daughter, Laodicea, nicknamed "Dicey," inherited her father's love of freedom. This is her story.

Because little was recorded of women's roles during the war, some people think stories like those of Dicey's heroic acts are legends. Yet for over two hundred years Laodicea Langston has been honored as a spunky teenage heroine.

Contents

Spunky Revolutionary War Heroine

1.
Close Call

Carrying sugar borrowed from a neighbor, Dicey trudged along the red clay road toward her home. *How could Uncle Frank turn Tory*! And Aunt Louisa? Dicey could still hear her aunt's words as she dipped the sugar from a stoneware jar.

"At least we'll have the king's protection," her aunt had said. "Heaven knows, there's no law in the Up Country these days."

It was true that the "Bloody Scouts," a band of cruel men who called themselves Tories, went about robbing and murdering Patriots. But even that couldn't make Dicey turn against her own

family in their fight for freedom.

At this very moment her brother James gathered with other Patriots beyond the Tyger River at a place called Elder Settlement. In his last sneak visit home, he whispered to her the location of his men.

Suddenly Dicey stumbled over a deep rut in the road. What she saw when she looked back up made her heart miss a beat. **Three strange men on horseback rounded the bend in the road.**

They did not wear hunting shirts and britches like her brothers and other Patriots. Dicey could tell by the scowls on their faces they were not friendly.

"Lookee here, Captain!" one of the men cried out. "This pretty little maid is old man Langston's daughter."

Dicey froze in her tracks. She must not let them know how frightened she was.

"Why, Captain," the man continued. "It's that pesky little Carolina rebel we talked about. No doubt she's been out carrying tales about our whereabouts to her rebel brothers."

The captain drew his horse's reins and came to a halt within two feet of Dicey. "We know where you've been, girl," he barked. "What news did you hear?"

Dicey pulled her shoulders back and looked the man in the eye. "I haven't heard anything," she said, "but if I had, I wouldn't tell you."

The captain's face turned red with anger. "We'll see about that!" He raised his gun with a jerk and pointed it at Dicey.

"Tell us what you know," he ordered, "or die where you stand."

Dicey's fear changed to anger. She grabbed the scarf at her neck and yanked it aside. "Go ahead, shoot." She tried to keep her voice from shaking. "I will not tell you a thing."

Just as the captain cocked the trigger, the third man thrust his arm out, knocking the captain's gun hand. The shot rang in the air.

"Would do no good to murder her," the man growled, "even if she is a rebel."

The captain shrugged his shoulders in disgust and snapped his horse's reins. The three strangers turned and galloped away.

Trembling all over, Dicey plopped down on the grassy roadside. She was just getting ready for a good cry when she thought of something.

A Tory party once broke into their home and carried off some of their possessions.

"What about this pewter bowl?" one of the Tories asked another.

"It'll make good bullets," the second answered.

Dicey caught her breath. Was the bullet that might have killed her from their own pewter bowl?

She pulled herself up. Mammy Hester, as she called their old slave, would be waiting for the sugar.

2.
The Warning

Twilight had gathered by the time Dicey reached home. She went straight to the kitchen and made herself busy. Her father must not find out that Bloody Scouts had pointed a gun at her on the way home. He would never let her out of his sight again.

She missed her brothers since they joined up to fight with the Patriots. The three of them had good times galloping their horses over the hills and rocky soil of their land.

"Wait up!" she would yell as the clap of their horses' hoofs echoed through the hills. But they hadn't waited, for they knew Dicey could catch up

with them if she put her mind to it.

Since the death of their mother when Dicey was young, her brothers had taken over the guidance of their small, black-eyed sister. Not only had they taught her to ride but to shoot a rifle as well. Solomon Langston knew little of bringing up a girl. He could only sit by and watch his daughter roam the woods with his sons. Besides, he was growing old.

As a younger man Solomon had served in several regiments. But now he was becoming feeble, and the fighting of neighbor against neighbor kept him worried. Next to his children, he loved his homeland most. He had instilled this love in his sons and daughter.

"Laodicea—" Solomon Langston's voice cut through Dicey's thoughts. "Come to the parlor."

Her father had called her by her given name! What was wrong?

Moments later Dicey stood before her father where he sat on the settee. Evening shadows fell across the parlor. In the sternest voice he could force himself to use with his daughter, he said,

"Laodicea, you know the Tories sometimes use our north field to train their soldiers."

Dicey nodded, her curiosity rising.

"The soldier in charge came here today." Her father's voice was as solemn as the ticking of the big clock on the mantle. "The Tory soldier called you—" Solomon Langston took a deep breath before continuing. "He called you a—a spy."

Dicey stopped breathing. Did her father know she gave secret messages to her brothers when they returned home under the cover of night? She must be careful of the words that passed her lips.

When she could hold her breath no longer, she blurted out, "But, Father, when I hear Tories are headed toward one of my brothers' camps, I must get word to them."

"No, Daughter, no." He lowered his head into his hands. His shoulders shook.

Dicey's heart ached to see her father so upset. Yet her voice grew loud in a way she never spoke to him. "Would you have my brothers killed?" she asked.

He looked up at her, his face twisted in worry. "Laodicea, you do not understand how serious this is. If you do anything the Tories do not like, they will put a watch on our home." His voice grew quiet. "Then when your brothers slip by to see us, they will be killed and our home plundered and destroyed."

Dicey sat down beside her father and put her arm around his shoulders. More than anything she wanted to be an obedient daughter. She would try. With all her might she would try.

For the next few weeks Dicey did her best to be indifferent to the fight for freedom going on around them. Then something happened.

3.
Dangerous Mission

Dicey sat in the bedroom of a friend whose family supported the Tory side of the war. She heard the mumble of men's voices in the parlor. Suddenly the parlor door swung open, and the voices became clearer.

One of the men said something about a "surprise attack." Dicey strained to hear.

She pretended to be interested in the shiny buckles on her friend's shoes, but her ears were tuned to the conversation coming from the adjoining room.

"On Elder Settlement!" one said. She heard it as plain as day.

"That's where brother James is!" her mind screamed. It was all she could do to keep still.

As quickly as she could, Dicey made an excuse to go home. Once out of sight of the house, she dashed down the dusty road. Her skirts and petticoats flailed about her legs. Her feet could not keep up with the whirling thoughts in her mind. What should she do? How could she disobey her father? He was already worried enough. Yet, if she didn't warn James, he and his men could be killed.

For the rest of the afternoon Dicey's mind churned. Mammy Hester gave her the job of watching the ham skewered onto the spit over the open fire in their kitchen. It was Dicey's responsibility to keep the spit turning so the meat would brown evenly on all sides.

Once she lost herself in thoughts of James

until she smelled something burning. Mammy Hester would be angry if she ruined the ham. Thank goodness it was only the drippings falling onto the glowing coals.

"If my father were not so old," she told herself, "he would be fighting against the Tories." Hadn't he taught his children to love freedom? That's why her brothers were away fighting.

And her mother? If she had lived, Dicey knew she would want her to save James.

By nightfall her frustration faded. She knew what she had to do. She had no choice but to warn James the Tories were on their way to Elder Settlement.

After supper, Dicey fidgeted as she watched her father nod in his rocker. When at last he bade her goodnight and went up to bed, she slipped outside. She had thought it over and made the decision to walk. It would take longer, but there was less chance she would be seen. On horseback, a Tory would surely spot her and be suspicious. On foot, she could hide in the woods.

Confident of the path she would take, Dicey set out toward Elder Settlement where James had whispered the Patriots would be camping.

A weak Carolina moon shone down, casting ghostly shadows across the wagon trail she tried to follow. Soon the trail plunged into thick dark woods. The cracking of twigs and the cries of animals were scary sounds. Familiar places seemed unfamiliar in the darkness. Dicey fought back feelings of panic.

Now and then she lifted her long skirts above the flooded fields and worked at keeping her balance on footlogs over marshland.

On she plodded, along unmarked roads and

through dripping underbrush until she reached the Tyger River. To her surprise, recent rains had flooded the shallow part where she and her brothers usually waded across. The rushing river had flooded its banks. The water whirled at her feet.

Dicey clinched her teeth and stuck in one foot. With each step the chilling water rose higher and higher. It whooshed around her until it reached her neck. Then without warning the current swirled her in a dizzying circle, sweeping her off her feet. Stunned and frightened, she lost her sense of direction.

What if the racing water of the cold, dark river dragged her away and James never got the warning?

She suddenly landed on the opposite shore, exhausted and half drowned. Shivering, she made her way to the shelter where she knew James and his men camped.

"Quickly," she called, "send your men to tell the people who live around here. The Tories are coming."

At first James's face showed shock at seeing his sister and hearing the news. Then his look turned to admiration.

"To tell you the truth, Sister," he said, "my men and I have just returned from a skirmish. We are faint with hunger and want of sleep."

"Then build a fire," Dicey said, "and I'll bake hoecakes. You can eat along the way."

"You're as wet as a drowned kitten," James said. "'Tis a shame you have to cook for us, Dicey, and that's the truth."

In the next breath he ordered his men to tear boards from their shelter and build a fire.

Soon the warming smell of bread browning in the frying pan filled the camp. Dicey stuffed hot bread into the soldiers' saddlebags, and off they clattered.

At daybreak Dicey reached home and hurried to the kitchen to help Mammy Hester with breakfast. It was as if she had not been away at all.

4.
A Daring Rescue

For a while things went smoothly in the Langston household. Then one fall day as Dicey and Mammy Hester worked on the back porch, drying apples, things changed. They had peeled the apples and sliced them into slender pieces. They were laying them on a table to dry when they heard the tramping of horses' hoofs.

By the time Dicey reached the front of the house, a Tory held her father against the parlor wall. Another held a musket, aimed at his chest. Other Tories watched.

Dicey rushed across the room and flung her arms around her father's neck.

"Get out of the way, girl!" the soldier with the gun shouted. "Unless you want to be shot with this old traitor."

"Shoot me if you dare!" Dicey shrieked. "But don't shoot a helpless old man, you coward."

The commanding officer stepped up. "The girl has spunk," he said. "Let the old man go."

The soldier cursed, lowered his gun, and glared at Dicey. The captain made a final warning about spying on Tories and carrying messages to the Patriots.

Dicey held her breath. Did the Tory captain know about her trip to warn James and his men at Elder Settlement? Would he say so in front of her father?

To her relief, the men stormed out, mounted their horses, and rode away.

5.
The Password

Battles and skirmishes continued all about the Up Country. When Dicey's brothers could do so, they slipped by the Langston home. During one of these quick visits, James left a rifle in Dicey's care.

"I will send for it," he told her. "But you must not let anyone have it unless he gives you the secret sign." He leaned over and whispered the password in his sister's ear.

Some time had passed when a group of Patriots commanded by Captain Thomas Springfield stopped at the Langston home. After Dicey greeted the group and offered them water and food, Captain Springfield said, "I have come for the rifle left in your care."

In her excitement Dicey ran inside and took the gun from its hiding place. Rushing back to the front door, she remembered she had not asked for the password. She stopped short, demanding, "Give me the secret word."

Captain Springfield had already stepped toward her. "You are too late, Miss Laodicea," he said. "You and the rifle are now in my command." He flashed his handsome smile and reached for the gun.

Dicey stepped back, cocked the rifle, and leveled the weapon at his head. "Oh, are we?" she asked. "Then come and get us."

Springfield's men broke into laughter.

Embarrassed, the captain sputtered the password, and Dicey handed over James's gun.

"I'll tell you what, boys," one of the men called out as they left. "James Langston is a good soldier, but he's no better a one than his sister."

6.
Happy Ending

After many more years of fighting, the Revolutionary War between the colonies and their mother country England was finally over. The colonists were free to rule themselves. Sadly, many men lost their lives in the fight for freedom. One of them was Dicey's brother, James.

Men who did return to their homes and families faced years of hardship. Houses, churches, and public buildings had been destroyed. Farmland had not been planted, and families were in need of flour and corn. Times were hard. It took decades for the colonies to recover.

As for Dicey, her story had a happy ending.

Captain Thomas Springfield must have admired the spunky young girl who held a rifle on him. When the war was over, he returned and asked her to marry him. She accepted.

Thomas and Dicey made their home near Travelers Rest, South Carolina, in what is now Greenville County. They lived there for many years surrounded by their children and grandchildren. Dicey died on May 23, 1837. She was seventy-one years old. Many descendants of their large family still live in the area.

Although the Springfield home no longer stands, a monument near the site honors Dicey. The inscription reads: "To her daring and courage many Patriots owe their lives." The monument was erected by the Nathanael Greene Chapter of the Daughters of the American Revolution in 1933. The base of the monument is made from the steps of the Langston home. The upright stone was a hearthstone inside their cabin. It is believed

the giant cedar growing beside the monument was planted by Dicey.

The grave of this teenage Revolutionary War heroine lies a short distance from the monument in a wooded area. At one time the grave was enclosed in a stone wall. It now lies in the open among other fieldstone markers, too weathered to read.

A marker placed at Dicey's grave by the Daughters of the American Revolution reads: "A Revolutionary War heroine who dared to risk her life because of her love for liberty."

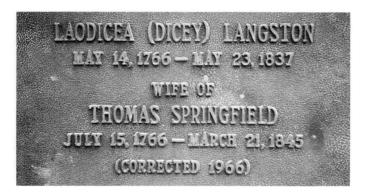

LAODICEA (DICEY) LANGSTON
MAY 14, 1766 — MAY 23, 1837
WIFE OF
THOMAS SPRINGFIELD
JULY 15, 1766 — MARCH 21, 1845
(CORRECTED 1966)

TRAVELERS REST

E
SI

Tyger R.

Enoree R.

LANGS
HOME

Saluda R.

Savannah R.

GEORGIA

South
Carolina

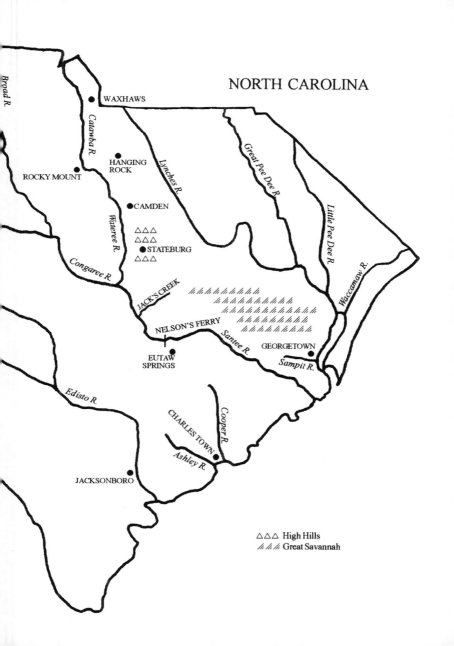

Words Needed for Understanding

adjoining — next to or close to each other

descendants — children and grandchildren and other family members to come

fidget — to move about restlessly

fieldstone — rough stones found in fields

flail — to beat or thrash about

hearthstone — stone flooring in front of a fireplace

hoecake — bread made of cornmeal

Loyalist — a colonist who is loyal to the king of England

Patriot — a person who loves his or her country; in this case, those individuals seeking freedom from English rule

pewter — a dull silver metal made primarily of tin

settee	a small sofa
skewered	fastened by piercing
skirmish	a fight between small troops of soldiers
spit	a thin pointed rod
spunk	courage
Tory	another name for Loyalist
Whig	another name for Patriot

Things to Do and Talk About

1. Explain why some colonists fought other colonists.

2. Colonists who fought on the side of the English wanted to be called Loyalists, not Tories. Why do you think they felt that way?

3. Try to find the origins of the words *Tory* and *Whig*?

4. Tories called the Patriots "rebels." What do you think of when you hear the word *rebel*? Would you like to be called a rebel? Why or why not?

5. What is the difference between a skirmish and a battle?

6. Why do you think fighting continued long after July 4, 1776, the day the Declaration of Independence was signed?

7. Did you know that more Revolutionary War battles were fought in South Carolina than in any other state? Can you find out how many battles

and skirmishes there were? Can you name some of the major battles? Which battle sites have become national parks?

8. Draw a map of South Carolina and put in the major rivers and battlesites. Be sure to include the Tyger River, which Dicey crossed.

9. There are people who think stories about some heroes and heroines are legends. What is a legend?

10. Why was Aunt Louisa glad her family made the decision to switch from being Patriots to Tories?

11. History does not tell us the password Dicey's brother whispered to her in order to keep his gun from getting in the wrong hands. What do you think it might have been?

12. Have you ever done anything that took spunk? What was it? Were you proud?

13. Act out scenes from Dicey's life for your class-mates.

Sources Used

Batson, Mann. *The Upper Part of Greenville County.* Taylors, SC: Faith Printing Company, 1993.

Dubose, Louise Jones. *South Carolina Distinguished Women of Laurens County.* Columbia, SC: R.L. Bryan, 1972.

Ellet, Elizabeth F. *Women of the American Revolution,* Vol. 1. New York: Haskell House Publishers, 1969.

Green, Harry C., and Mary W. Green. *Pioneer Mothers in America.* New York: Putnam, 1912.

Hilborn, Nat, and Sam Hilborn. *Battleground of Freedom.* Columbia, SC: Sandlapper Press, 1970.

Lamb, Bessie Pode. "Geneological History." Private papers, Greenville County Library, n.d.

Langston, Obal Elbridge. *Langston Heritage to Posterity.* 1988. From the personal library of Doris Robertson Wood, descendant of Dicey Langston.

Sickels, Eleanor. *In Calico and Crinoline.* New York: Viking, 1935.

About the Author

Idella Bodie was born in Ridge Spring, South Carolina. She received her degree in English from Columbia College and taught high school English and creative writing for thirty-one years.

Ms. Bodie's first book was published in 1971, and she has been writing books for young readers ever since. This is her sixteenth book.

Ms. Bodie lives in Aiken with her husband Jim. When she is not busy with research, writing, or public appearances, she enjoys reading and gardening.

Books by Idella Bodie

HEROES AND HEROINES OF THE AMERICAN REVOLUTION

The Man Who Loved the Flag

The Secret Message

The Revolutionary Swamp Fox

The Fighting Gamecock

OTHERS

Carolina Girl:
A Writer's Beginning

Ghost in the Capitol

Ghost Tales for Retelling

A Hunt for Life's Extras:
The Story of Archibald Rutledge

The Mystery of Edisto Island

The Mystery of the Pirate's Treasure

The Secret of Telfair Inn

South Carolina Women

Stranded!

Trouble at Star Fort

Whopper